MYTHICAL · MAZES ·

A COLLECTION OF AMAZING MYTHICAL MAZES

Retold by
Dugald Steer

Illustrated by
Lorna Hussey • Nick Harris
Nick Hewetson • Lee Stannard
and Bill Le Fever

Designed by
Janie Louise Hunt

FENN

Fenn Publishing Company Ltd

.Introduction.

JOIN some of the most famous figures
of legend on their epic journeys in ten timeless
tales of adventure, from North America, from Europe,
Africa and the Far East. Recapture some of the thrill
of their exploits by solving the intricate, beautifully
illustrated mazes that accompany each story. Can you
help Theseus through the dark corridors of the
Labyrinth to battle the Minotaur? Can you find Sir
Gawain's path to the mysterious Green Knight? Can
you lead Poia to the Sun's lodge and home again?

Adventure awaits you over the page. Good
luck, and may the gods be with you!

· The Myths ·

THOR
AND THE FROST GIANT

ONE of the greatest Viking gods was
Thor, the god of thunder. In one of his most exciting
adventures he embarks on a journey to Giant Land to
retrieve his magic hammer, stolen by Thrym, a frost giant.
He is helped in his quest by Freyja, a goddess promised
in marriage to Thrym if the hammer is returned,
Loki, a shape-changer, and Heimdall, the
guardian of the rainbow bridge.

Can you find the one continuous path that leads
Thor to each of his helpers before he reaches
Thrym in Giant Land?

LOKI

THRYM

THOR

HEIMDALL

FREYJA

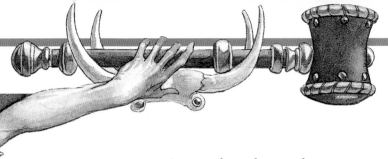

LONG AGO, in ancient times, people believed that the Norse gods ruled the world. One of the most famous and most popular was Thor, the god of thunder. Thor was a mighty warrior - huge and incredibly strong. His fiery temper matched his flame-red hair and beard. But he was gentle and fun-loving and rarely stayed angry for long. Master of thunder and lightning, Thor could whip up great storms just by blowing through his beard. Thor was also the god of law and order and he protected Asgard, the home of the gods, against its enemies. He also looked after the homes of the Norsemen on Earth. To help him in his work, Thor used magic weapons. The most famous of these was his remarkable hammer, Mjöllnir, which always hit its target and protected people from danger. On Earth, Norsemen even gave tiny hammers to babies and brides as good luck charms. Mjöllnir was Thor's most prized possession and he was proud of it.

So, you can imagine how Thor felt when he woke up one morning to find that his hammer had been stolen. He immediately went to seek help from the other gods.

"I will find it for you," said Loki, who could change his shape at will.

"Here," said Freyja, the goddess of love and beauty. "Take my falcon skin. It will help you fly more swiftly than the wind."

Loki soon returned, but the news was not good. The hammer had been stolen by Thrym, a frost giant. He was willing to return the hammer, but on one condition - Freyja must become his bride. Thor and Loki urged Freyja to go to Thrym.

"No! Never!" said Freyja, shedding golden tears. "I cannot be his wife."

"What choice have we," said Loki. "We *must* get Thor's hammer back."

"Wait," said the god Heimdall, who disliked Loki. "I have a plan."

The gods listened in amazement as Heimdall explained how they could trick Thrym and retrieve the hammer. Thor must dress in bridal clothes and pretend to be Freyja. Loki, who was eager to go along and see the fun, would be his bridesmaid.

Willingly Freyja found flowing robes to disguise the gods and veils to mask their faces. Then Freyja called for her best chariot to carry the two gods on their long journey.

It was a wild and windy journey to the land of the frost giants. Thor and Loki were relieved when they saw the lights of Thrym's hall twinkling before them. They leapt from the chariot and hammered on the door. The door was flung wide and Thrym and his sister welcomed them in.

"Come," commanded Thrym, taking Thor's

hand. "The wedding banquet is laid. We have been waiting for you – my bride."

They were led to the head of the table and Thor was seated in the bride's place. Then the banquet began. Thor was so hungry that he almost gave himself away by eating masses of food. Loki, seeing Thrym's astonished glance, swiftly explained "Freyja's" hunger.

"My lord," he said. "My mistress Freyja has been so excited at the thought of seeing you that she has not eaten for days!" Thrym smiled with delight.

"We will wait no longer," he said. "Bring Mjöllnir to bless the bride." The magical hammer was carried in and laid before Thrym. Turning towards his bride, Thrym placed the hammer on her knees as tradition decreed.

With a great roar, Thor threw off his veil and grabbed Mjöllnir. Whirling the hammer above his head, Thor stood and faced the terrified giants. The giants turned and fled, but not before Thor had killed many of them, including Thrym.

Thor and Loki returned to Asgard in triumph with Mjöllnir held aloft as their sign of victory. The giants would never trouble the gods again until the last battle, Ragnarok.

THE
WANDERINGS
OF ISIS

THE MYTHS of the Ancient Egyptians were recorded
in hieroglyphic writing on the walls of their great pyramids,
tombs and temples. Many of these myths tell of Isis and her
husband, Osiris. They were among the most important gods
of Ancient Egypt. Osiris was the Egyptian god of the dead.
Every Egyptian hoped to be reborn after death in Osiris'
kingdom, the land of the dead that lay towards the
setting sun. In this story, Osiris is killed by his
treacherous brother, Seth.

To complete this maze you must help
Isis find her way through the corridors
of the Great Pyramid to reach Osiris.

ACCORDING to legend, Isis and Osiris were the first rulers of Egypt. They taught the people about farming, law and religion. Many stories are told about them, but this one is perhaps the most famous.

The brother of Osiris was called Seth. Seth was very jealous of Osiris and his wife Isis and he was always trying to make himself king in their place. One day he secretly built a beautiful but very strong chest and made it to fit Osiris exactly. Seth then invited Osiris to a feast. After the meal was over Seth showed his guests the chest and said that he would give it to the person it fitted best. Everyone took turns laying down in the chest but it didn't fit anyone. At last it came to Osiris' turn. As soon as he had got into the chest, Seth slammed the lid shut, locked it and sealed it up. He carried it down to the Nile and flung it into the river, which soon carried it far out into the Mediterranean Sea.

The chest was eventually washed up in

Lebanon near the ancient city of Byblos. A storm carried it far up the beach and left it in the branches of a young sapling. The sapling became a mighty tree that grew around the chest. The king of Byblos was so impressed with the tree that he had it cut down and finely carved to make one of the pillars of his new palace.

Isis, meanwhile, had given birth to a son whom she named Horus. As soon as she learned what had happened to her husband, she cut her hair and dressed herself in black mourning clothes. She took Horus to be looked after in the land of Chemmis, where Seth would not be able to find him, then set out to look for Osiris.

The wanderings of Isis took her through many countries and she had many adventures. One day she heard about what had happened to the chest which contained her husband. She travelled to Byblos and it was not long before she had been put in charge of nursing the queen's baby son.

In the palace Isis transformed herself into a swallow. She flew round and round the pillar that contained Seth's chest sobbing and wailing for her husband. The noise woke the queen who became worried about her baby and immediately came to see what was happening. Isis explained to her who she really was. The queen gave Isis the pillar and Isis cut it open, took out the chest and returned to Egypt with it. There, she hid the chest in a marsh and went back to Chemmis to fetch Horus.

One day while Isis was away, Seth went out hunting and found the chest he had locked his enemy in. He took out the body of Osiris and cut it into fourteen pieces, which he hid in different places in Egypt.

When Isis returned she was determined to find all the pieces of Osiris and so her wanderings began again.

Helped by her sister Nephthys, she collected all the pieces of Osiris except one, which had been eaten by a fish. She embalmed them, making the first mummy of a dead king. Horus claimed his father's throne from the wicked Seth and raised a magnificent temple to his father. This was how Osiris came to be the god of the dead.

SEDNA

AND THE BIRD SPIRIT

The Inuit people of
northern Canada live in a world of ice and snow.

Traditionally they made their living as hunters and fishermen.
Sea creatures, such as whales, seals and walruses, sea birds,
such as the fulmar, and indeed the very sea itself have
always been important to them.

Many of their legends tell of the constant battle
that the Inuit must wage with the elements.
Sedna is the Inuit goddess of the sea and the animals
of the sea and the Inuit respect her greatly.
This story tells how she first became a goddess.

To complete this maze you must help Sedna's father, Angusta,
to find where she is held prisoner by her husband,
the bird spirit, in the land of the birds. To find the route
you must follow the hidden path of the sea creatures.

MANY LEGENDS tell how the animals were created. This one tells us how the seals, walruses, and whales came to be.

Sedna was a beautiful young Inuit girl who lived happily with her father, Angusta. Because she was so beautiful all the young Inuit men wanted to marry her, but whenever they asked her, she would always reply, "No, thank you. I am quite happy living with my father. Why should I get married?"

Then one day, when her father was away, a handsome young hunter arrived in his kayak, an Inuit canoe. He was dressed in rich furs and he carried a long, ivory spear. He was so handsome that Sedna couldn't help falling in love with him. Even so, she didn't go out to meet him but watched him shyly from the entrance to her tent.

The hunter stayed off-shore in his kayak. "Come away with me, Sedna, to the land of the birds!" he called. "It is a beautiful land where you will never be hungry. You will lie on the warmest bear skins, and have whatever you wish."

At first Sedna stayed near her tent but she was soon enchanted by the hunter's description of his country and of the wonderful life she would have there. At last she went down to the sea and climbed into the young man's kayak.

It did not take Sedna and the young hunter long to reach the land of the birds. When they got there, to Sedna's horror the young man confessed that he had played a trick on her. "I am not a man," he said. " I am really a bird spirit. And I love you."

By this time Angusta had returned home. He was very worried about Sedna and so he set out to find her. When he reached the land of the birds, the weeping Sedna told him how she had been tricked. The bird spirit was away from home and so Angusta quickly carried Sedna down to his kayak and they began to paddle back home.

The bird spirit heard what was happening and realised that Sedna was escaping.

Immediately he changed into a man, got into his kayak and began to chase after Sedna.

As the bird spirit approached them, Angusta hid Sedna under some furs.

"Let me see my wife!" cried the bird spirit. Angusta shook his head firmly.

Suddenly the angry bird spirit left his kayak, flying up in the shape of an enormous fulmar, a kind of seabird. Uttering furious cries he swooped overhead for a few minutes and then disappeared into the distance.

Sedna was a good swimmer and, when Angusta had thrown her out of the boat, she caught hold of the side. Angusta had to chop at her fingers once, twice, three times with his ivory axe until she was unable to hold on any more. When he cut at her fingers the first time, the pieces he cut off turned into the seals. The second time the pieces became the walruses. And the third time they became the mighty whales.

Just then a huge storm came up and Angusta's little boat was tossed about by the gigantic Arctic waves. Angusta finally realised what a powerful being the bird spirit was. Terrified, he decided that the only way to calm the storm would be to sacrifice Sedna.

The sea became quiet and Angusta returned home, saddened and exhausted by all that had happened. Falling into a deep sleep, he did not notice the tide rising and rising until suddenly he too was washed into the cold sea.

JASON
AND THE GOLDEN FLEECE

BEFORE the invention of writing, a storyteller had to learn all of his stories by heart. Many of the first tales are lost to us because no record was kept of them. The people of Greece were among the first to write down their tales and because of this many of their myths and legends still survive. In this tale the hero, Jason, travels in his ship, the *Argo,* in search of the Golden Fleece, which was the skin of a magical ram.

See if you can help Jason guide the *Argo* through the dangerous seas that lead to the terrible dragon that guards the Golden Fleece.

MANY OF THE LEGENDS of the Ancient Greeks tell how things were invented, or when they first happened. The story of *Jason and the Golden Fleece* is about the very first ship. It is quite possible that, as with many legends, the story is based on something which really happened.

Jason was the son of King Aeson. He was only a boy when his father died and his wicked uncle Pelias made himself king. When Jason grew up, Pelias decided to send Jason on such a dangerous journey that he would never return to claim his kingdom.

"Have you heard of the Golden Fleece, Jason?" asked Pelias. "It is the skin of a magical golden ram. It is kept in the land of Colchis, where it is guarded by a dragon that never sleeps. Bring me the Golden Fleece and you can become king!"

Colchis was on the eastern shores of the Black Sea, a long way from Greece, and so Jason went to see a man called Argus, who was a boatbuilder.

"Build me a ship that is big enough for fifty heroes!" he said.

Argus wasn't sure that it was possible but, after a lot of work, the ship was finally ready. Jason called it the *Argo*. The crew included many famous Greek heroes and together they became known as the Argonauts.

To get to the Black Sea the Argonauts had to sail through the Clashing Rocks. These rocks floated on the surface of the sea and crashed together, destroying anything which tried to pass. As the *Argo* approached, Jason released a white dove which flew between the rocks, losing only a few tail feathers as they clashed together. When the rocks sprang apart again the Argonauts rowed as fast as they could, just managing to get through before the huge boulders came together again.

After a long voyage the *Argo* arrived in Colchis and Jason went to see the king, Aeetes, and told him why he had come.

"I will let you have the Golden Fleece if you can do two simple things," said King Aeetes. "You must plough and sow one of my fields."

Jason agreed but he soon found out that to plough the field he would have to yoke together two huge fire-breathing bulls. He would then have to sow the field with dragon's teeth and a crop of armed warriors would spring up from the teeth and attack him.

Luckily, King Aeetes' daughter Medea had fallen in love with Jason. Medea was a sorceress and she secretly taught Jason some of her magic.

The bulls were brought to the field, breathing

flames and bellowing ferociously. Jason stood before them and uttered Medea's charm. He was able to pat the bulls, speak soothingly to them and slip the yoke over their shoulders. He had no trouble in ploughing the field.

Jason quickly went to find the Golden Fleece. When he arrived he sprinkled the dragon with a potion Medea had given him. The enormous beast was soon snoring soundly and Jason took the Golden Fleece easily.

Next Jason took the bag of dragon's teeth and sowed them. Immediately fifty warriors leapt up and began to attack him. He threw a stone amongst them and uttered another charm. Immediately the warriors began to attack each other until they were all dead.

Jason returned to the *Argo* with Medea and the Fleece and the Argonauts rowed back home.

Jason lost little time in laying the Golden Fleece before the surprised Pelias. He soon became king and he ruled his kingdom wisely for many years.

TALIESIN

The Mabinogion is the name
of a group of tales from Wales, in
the British Isles. These stories come from
the traditions of the Celts. They were
handed down from generation to
generation by professional storytellers, or
bards, before eventually being written
down by Christian monks. They are
tales filled with heroic deeds,

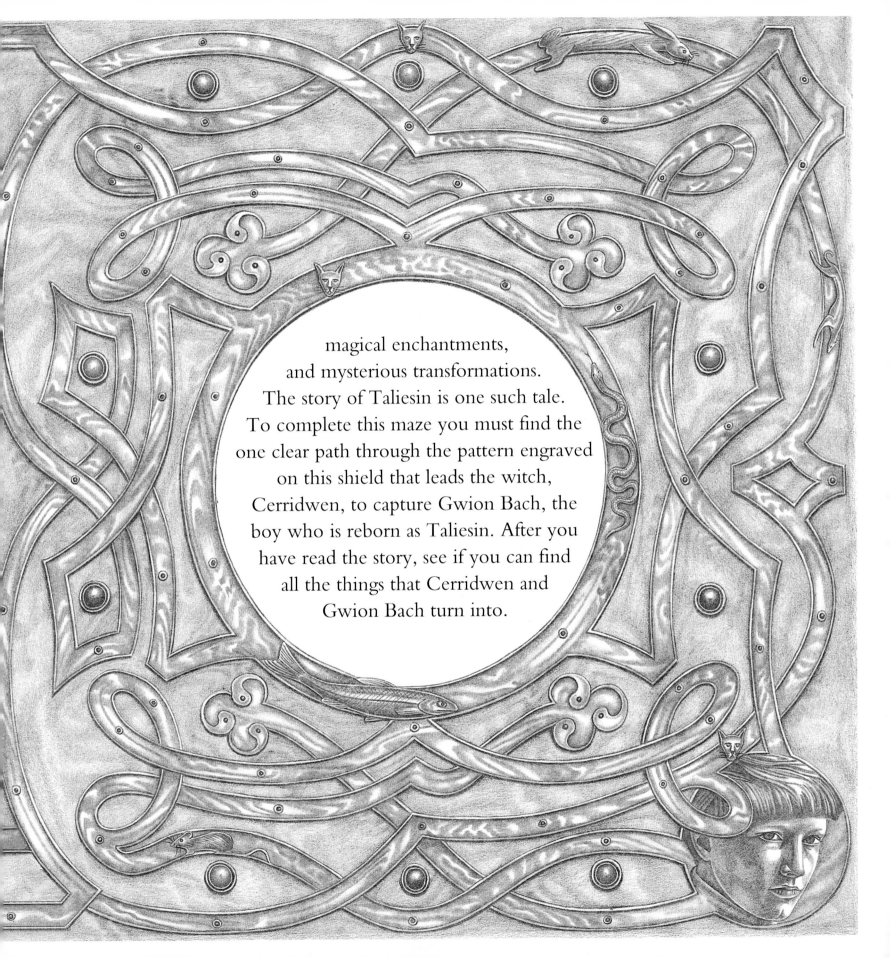

magical enchantments,
and mysterious transformations.
The story of Taliesin is one such tale.
To complete this maze you must find the
one clear path through the pattern engraved
on this shield that leads the witch,
Cerridwen, to capture Gwion Bach, the
boy who is reborn as Taliesin. After you
have read the story, see if you can find
all the things that Cerridwen and
Gwion Bach turn into.

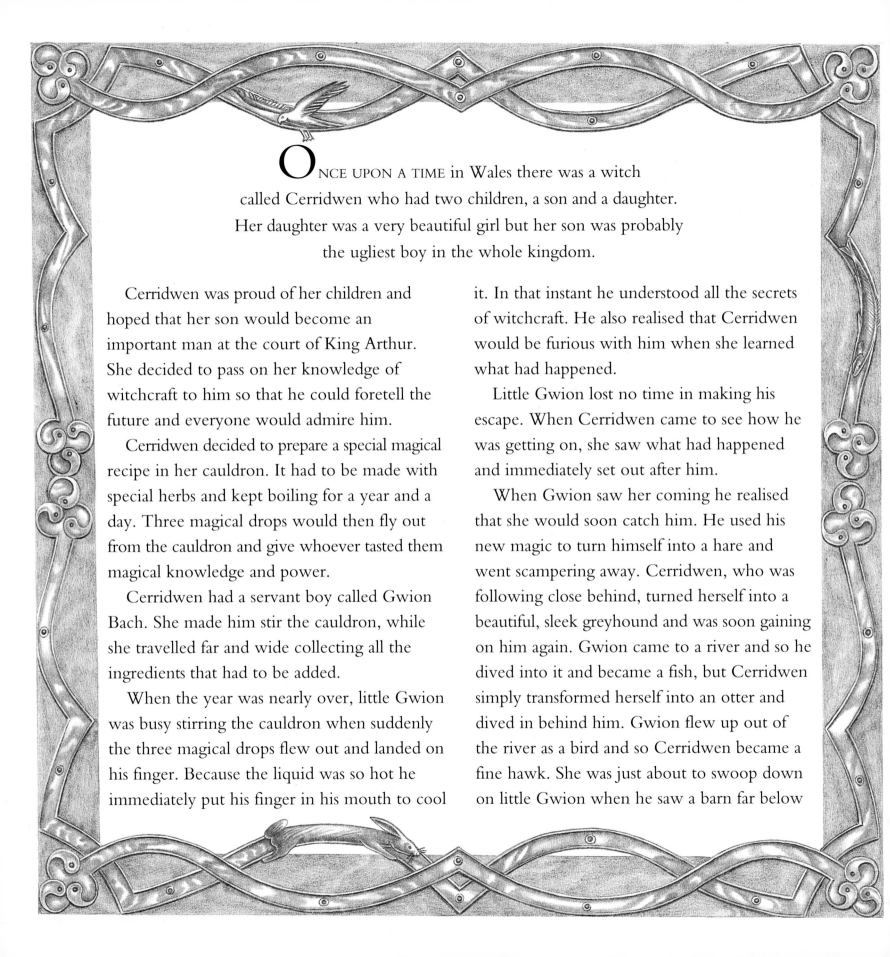

ONCE UPON A TIME in Wales there was a witch
called Cerridwen who had two children, a son and a daughter.
Her daughter was a very beautiful girl but her son was probably
the ugliest boy in the whole kingdom.

Cerridwen was proud of her children and hoped that her son would become an important man at the court of King Arthur. She decided to pass on her knowledge of witchcraft to him so that he could foretell the future and everyone would admire him.

Cerridwen decided to prepare a special magical recipe in her cauldron. It had to be made with special herbs and kept boiling for a year and a day. Three magical drops would then fly out from the cauldron and give whoever tasted them magical knowledge and power.

Cerridwen had a servant boy called Gwion Bach. She made him stir the cauldron, while she travelled far and wide collecting all the ingredients that had to be added.

When the year was nearly over, little Gwion was busy stirring the cauldron when suddenly the three magical drops flew out and landed on his finger. Because the liquid was so hot he immediately put his finger in his mouth to cool

it. In that instant he understood all the secrets of witchcraft. He also realised that Cerridwen would be furious with him when she learned what had happened.

Little Gwion lost no time in making his escape. When Cerridwen came to see how he was getting on, she saw what had happened and immediately set out after him.

When Gwion saw her coming he realised that she would soon catch him. He used his new magic to turn himself into a hare and went scampering away. Cerridwen, who was following close behind, turned herself into a beautiful, sleek greyhound and was soon gaining on him again. Gwion came to a river and so he dived into it and became a fish, but Cerridwen simply transformed herself into an otter and dived in behind him. Gwion flew up out of the river as a bird and so Cerridwen became a fine hawk. She was just about to swoop down on little Gwion when he saw a barn far below

him. The floor of the barn was covered with grains of wheat so he flew down and became one grain of wheat amongst many thousands. Cerridwen turned herself into a large black hen and scratched and pecked at the wheat until she had eaten it all up, including little Gwion.

Nine months later Cerridwen gave birth to Gwion as a baby son. She tied him up in a little leather bag and threw him into the river.

Near the river lived a poor nobleman called Elphin, who was a very unlucky man. One day he went down to the weir on the river, to see if he could find any fish, but all he found was

the little leather bag containing the child.

"Other men find fish here," said the keeper of the weir. "You must be an unlucky man."

Elphin did not listen to this but simply opened the bag and saw baby Gwion. "Look!" he cried "See how the child's hair shines! I shall call him Taliesin." Elphin took the baby home and brought him up as his own son. From an early age Taliesin would surprise everyone with his knowledge, his skill as a bard and his ability to foretell the future. In time he became the greatest of all the bards and magicians in that kingdom, and indeed in many others besides.

SIGURD
AND THE DRAGON

The Viking storytellers, or skalds, told many epic tales,
called sagas. They were stories of battles and adventures and they
often told the story of one family through several generations.
The story of the hero Sigurd and Fafnir the dragon is part of
the Volsung Saga which tells of a Viking family called the Volsungs.
Sigurd, one of the Volsungs, wishes to avenge his father who has
been killed, but first he must help his friend and teacher,
Reginn, to kill Fafnir.

To complete this maze, you must help Sigurd and
Reginn find their way to the stream where
Fafnir comes to drink everyday.

SIGURD AND REGINN

HIALPREK

HREIDMAR

FAFNIR

FAFNIR was a fearsome dragon. He lived in a dark cave on a desolate plain called Greta Heath, guarding his hoard of treasure. He had not always been a dragon. Long before, he had been a man. He had lived peacefully with his father Hreimdar and his two brothers, Otter and Reginn.

Fafnir's brother Otter was a shape-shifter and he often took on the shape of an otter, which was how he got his name. One morning he was sitting by a waterfall, eating a fish, when the gods Odin, Hönir, and Loki passed by.

Loki loved mischief. Seeing Otter sitting there, he thought he was a real otter and threw a stone at him and killed him. The three gods skinned Otter and continued on their way until they reached Hreimdar's house. Hreimdar immediately recognised his son. He demanded that the gods pay weregild - a price for his son, otherwise the law would give him the right to kill Loki.

"I want enough gold to cover my son's skin! That is the weregild!" he said.

Loki knew that a rich dwarf called Andvari lived near the waterfall. Loki threatened to kill Andvari unless he gave Loki all of his treasure to his very last gem.

"If you take my treasure I will put a curse on it!" cried Andvari angrily. "It will bring bad luck to all who own it!"

Loki laughed and took the treasure to Hreimdar. It was just enough to cover the otter skin.

As time went by Fafnir thought about the gold more and more. He wanted it for himself and, one day, he killed his father and took all the treasure with him to the cave on Greta Heath.

He spent so much time watching over it that he gradually turned into a horrible, flame-breathing dragon.

Fafnir's brother Reginn could not avenge his father's death. He went to live with a king called Hialprek, where he found work as a smith.

One day a boy called Sigurd came to live with King Hialprek, and Reginn became his teacher. Sigurd's father had been cruelly killed, and Sigurd wanted revenge.

Reginn promised to make Sigurd a sword if he would agree to kill Fafnir.

Sigurd agreed but he was so strong that when he hit his new sword against an anvil to test it, the sword simply broke in two. The same thing happened to a second sword Reginn made. Sigurd had

an idea. He gave Reginn the broken pieces of his father's sword. It had been a special gift from Odin. Reginn took the pieces and soon he had forged a sword that no one could break. It was the best sword in the world.

Sigurd and Reginn travelled to Greta Heath. They found a path which Fafnir often came down to drink at a little stream. Sigurd dug out a pit and hid there until Fafnir came slithering above him. With one mighty lunge he pierced the dragon to the heart.

When the dragon was dead, Sigurd asked Reginn if he would like any of the gold.

"That gold has a curse on it, Sigurd!" said Reginn. "But the dragon's heart is magic. Give it to me to eat!"

Sigurd cut out the dragon's heart, and began to cook it for Reginn. When he thought it was cooked, he tasted it and found he was able to understand the language of the birds.

In the meantime, Andvari's curse was beginning to work on Reginn. He decided that he did want the gold after all. He crept up behind Sigurd with a knife.

"Look out, Sigurd!" called the birds. Sigurd turned just in time, and killed Reginn.

POIA'S JOURNEY TO THE SUN

Poia's tale was told by the Blackfoot people,
a Native American tribe who had hunting grounds in
Canada and on the Great Plains of the northern United States.
On his journey Poia is helped by several animals. Native Americans
have a great respect for animals and they feature in many of their stories.

To complete this maze you must help Poia travel on his adventure. Your
trail must take you via a wolf, a bear, a badger, a wolverine and two swans.
Then you must cross the sea and find a warrior's weapons, a warrior and
then a tepee. From there you must go to a shore, find some birds and
return to the tepee. Next collect two raven's feathers and cross
the Milky Way, taking the shortest route back to Poia
and his bride. At no point must you go back
on yourself. Happy hunting!

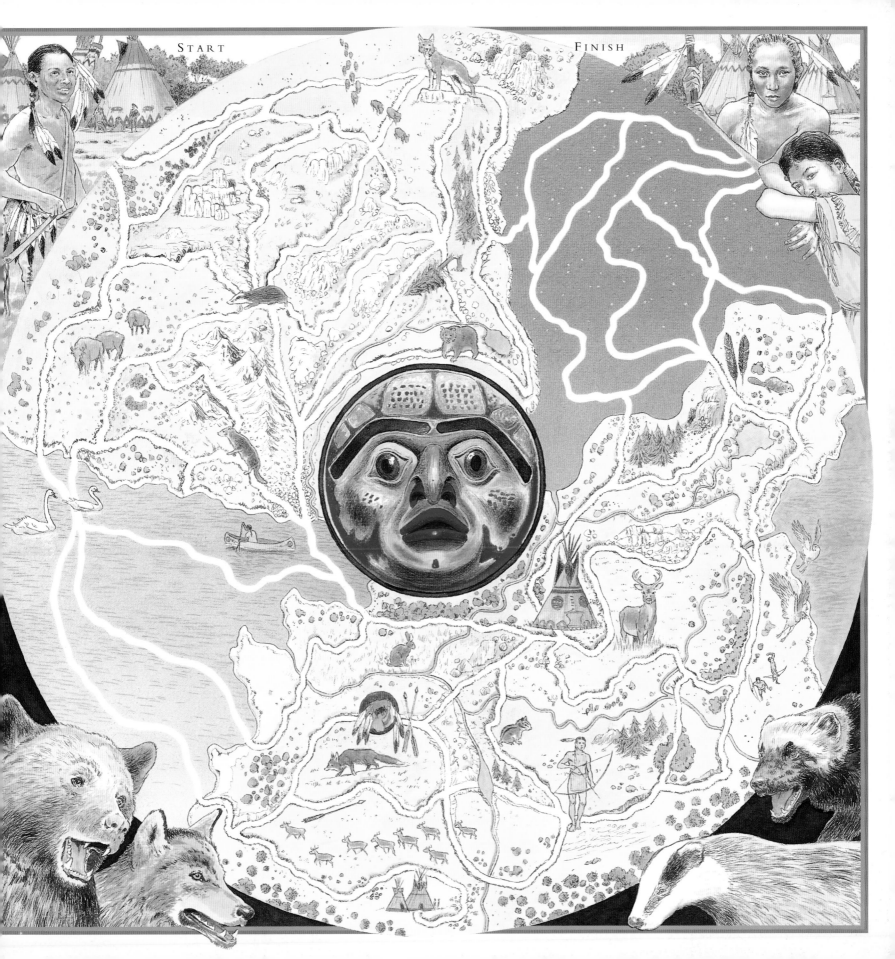

START

FINISH

THE MEDICINE LODGE is an important part of the Blackfoot Indians' traditional way of life. This story tells of the first time the Blackfoot people learned about the Medicine Lodge.

Once there was a beautiful girl who lived in a fine lodge with her mother and father. Many strong young warriors came to seek her hand in marriage but she refused all of them. Her father became angry and asked her why she was so obstinate. She replied that she could not marry because the Sun had come to her and told her:

"Listen. Do not marry. You are mine."

Now it so happened that in their camp there lived a very poor young man named Poia, which means 'Scarface'. He did indeed have a horrible scar on his face and the other young men were always teasing him about it. One day Poia decided to ask the girl to marry him. To his surprise she agreed – but only if he asked the Sun first. Poia had no idea where the Sun lived, but a kind old lady gave him food and moccasins and he set out.

After a while Poia met a wolf. He asked the wolf where the Sun lived. The wolf said he did not know and told him to ask a bear. The bear thought that a badger might know, but the badger didn't know either and said Poia should ask a wolverine. When Poia found the wolverine he directed Poia on a trail that led to a vast ocean. Poia had never seen such a huge quantity of water and had no idea how to cross it.

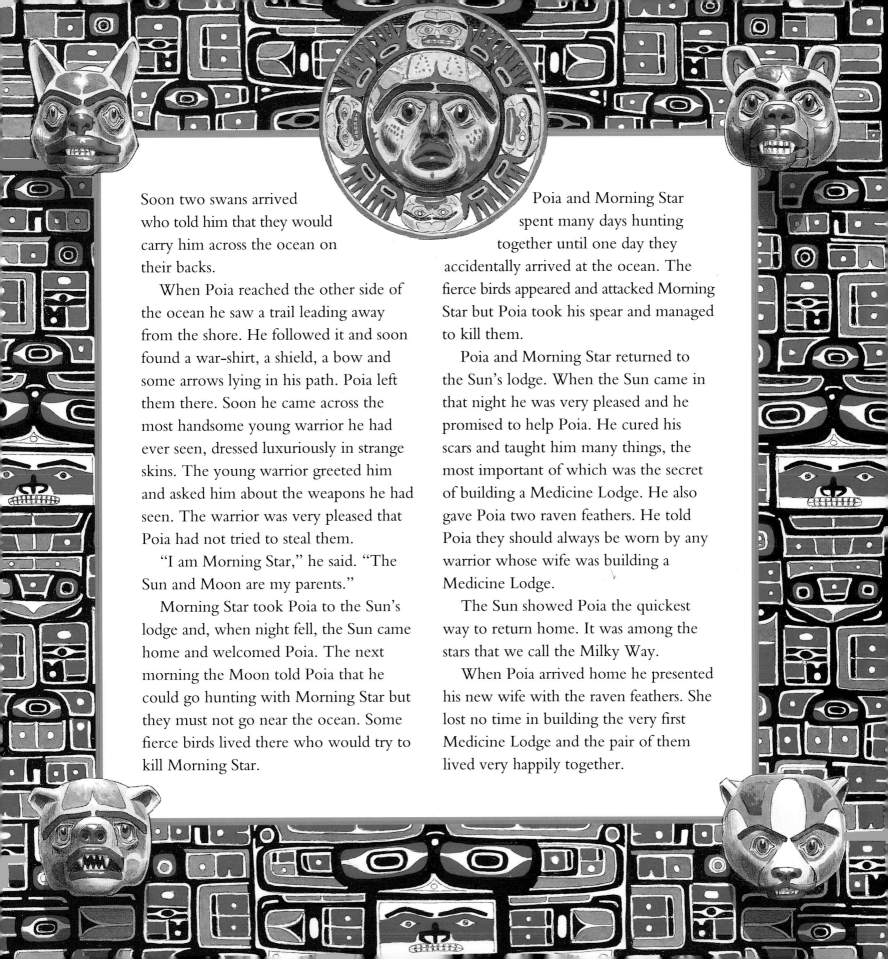

Soon two swans arrived who told him that they would carry him across the ocean on their backs.

When Poia reached the other side of the ocean he saw a trail leading away from the shore. He followed it and soon found a war-shirt, a shield, a bow and some arrows lying in his path. Poia left them there. Soon he came across the most handsome young warrior he had ever seen, dressed luxuriously in strange skins. The young warrior greeted him and asked him about the weapons he had seen. The warrior was very pleased that Poia had not tried to steal them.

"I am Morning Star," he said. "The Sun and Moon are my parents."

Morning Star took Poia to the Sun's lodge and, when night fell, the Sun came home and welcomed Poia. The next morning the Moon told Poia that he could go hunting with Morning Star but they must not go near the ocean. Some fierce birds lived there who would try to kill Morning Star.

Poia and Morning Star spent many days hunting together until one day they accidentally arrived at the ocean. The fierce birds appeared and attacked Morning Star but Poia took his spear and managed to kill them.

Poia and Morning Star returned to the Sun's lodge. When the Sun came in that night he was very pleased and he promised to help Poia. He cured his scars and taught him many things, the most important of which was the secret of building a Medicine Lodge. He also gave Poia two raven feathers. He told Poia they should always be worn by any warrior whose wife was building a Medicine Lodge.

The Sun showed Poia the quickest way to return home. It was among the stars that we call the Milky Way.

When Poia arrived home he presented his new wife with the raven feathers. She lost no time in building the very first Medicine Lodge and the pair of them lived very happily together.

SEA-GIRL
AND THE DRAGON KING'S DAUGHTER

THE Ancient Chinese believed that
the Earth was surrounded by four great
oceans. Each ocean was ruled over by a
mighty Dragon King who controlled
the rain. The Chinese people prayed to
the Dragon Kings for more rain when
there was a drought and for less when
there were floods!

In this story Sea-Girl, with the help
of the Dragon King's daughter,
sets out to find the key that will unlock
the water her starving people so badly
need to save their crops.

To complete this maze you must
trace Sea-Girl's path to the key,
which is hidden in the Dragon King's
treasury. On your way you must pass a
goose beside a lake, three parrots in a
tree, a peacock, the Dragon King's
daughter and an eagle.

SEA-GIRL lived with her father.
All the people in her part of the China were starving
because it had not rained for so long that their crops could not grow.
There was no water in the streams or wells and no one knew what to do.

One day, Sea-Girl had climbed up a mountain to cut bamboo when, to her surprise, she found an enormous lake of the clearest, purest water she had ever seen.

The next day Sea-Girl climbed back up the mountain with an axe, determined to cut a canal that would let the water from the clear lake run down into the dry valley. But no matter how hard she tried she couldn't make a single mark on the ground with her axe. Exhausted, she sat down under a tree desperately trying to think what else she could do.

At that moment a wild goose appeared beside her. To Sea-Girl's surprise it spoke to her.

"To open the waters of this lake is easy," said the goose. "But you need a golden key."

Before Sea-Girl could ask where she might find the key to open the waters of the lake the goose had flown off. Before long she saw three parrots sitting up in the trees.

"You must go to the third daughter of the

Dragon King," said the parrots, who also flew off before Sea-Girl could ask where the third daughter might be found.

Sea-Girl wondered how she would find the third daughter of the Dragon King. She looked up and saw a beautiful peacock.

"I know where the Dragon King's daughter lives," called the peacock. "I will show you the way. Follow me!"

As the peacock flew ahead of Sea-Girl he told her that the third daughter of the Dragon King loved folk songs. Sea-Girl began to sing all the songs she knew.

She had been singing for three days when the third daughter of the Dragon King suddenly appeared before her.

"Your songs are beautiful," said the Dragon King's daughter. "But why are you here? Where have you come from?"

Sea-Girl told the Dragon King's daughter about her search for the golden key that would unlock the waters of the lake on the mountain.

"Ah," said the Dragon King's daughter. "That key is in my father's treasury. But that treasury is guarded by a sleeping eagle who will wake up and kill anyone who goes there except my father himself."

Sea-Girl insisted that she had to try and enter the treasury. How else could the people be saved? The Dragon King's daughter showed her the way.

Sea-Girl and the Dragon King's daughter sat outside the treasury and began to sing

folk songs. The eagle woke up, heard the lovely music and came to listen. Sea-Girl saw her chance and slipped into the treasury.

Inside there was a huge quantity of gold and gems but Sea-Girl was only interested in finding the golden key. After a long search she found it. Quickly, Sea-Girl and the Dragon King's

daughter left the palace. As soon as the Dragon King's daughter stopped singing, the eagle returned to the treasury and fell asleep.

Soon the two girls had reached the mountain. Sea-Girl unlocked the lake and the water poured out. After a short time the Dragon King's daughter told her to lock up the lake again, or the whole land would be drowned.

When the Dragon King discovered that the key had been taken he was so angry that he banished his third daughter for ever. She went to live with Sea-Girl and the pair of them lived very happily, singing their folk songs together and walking among the mountains.

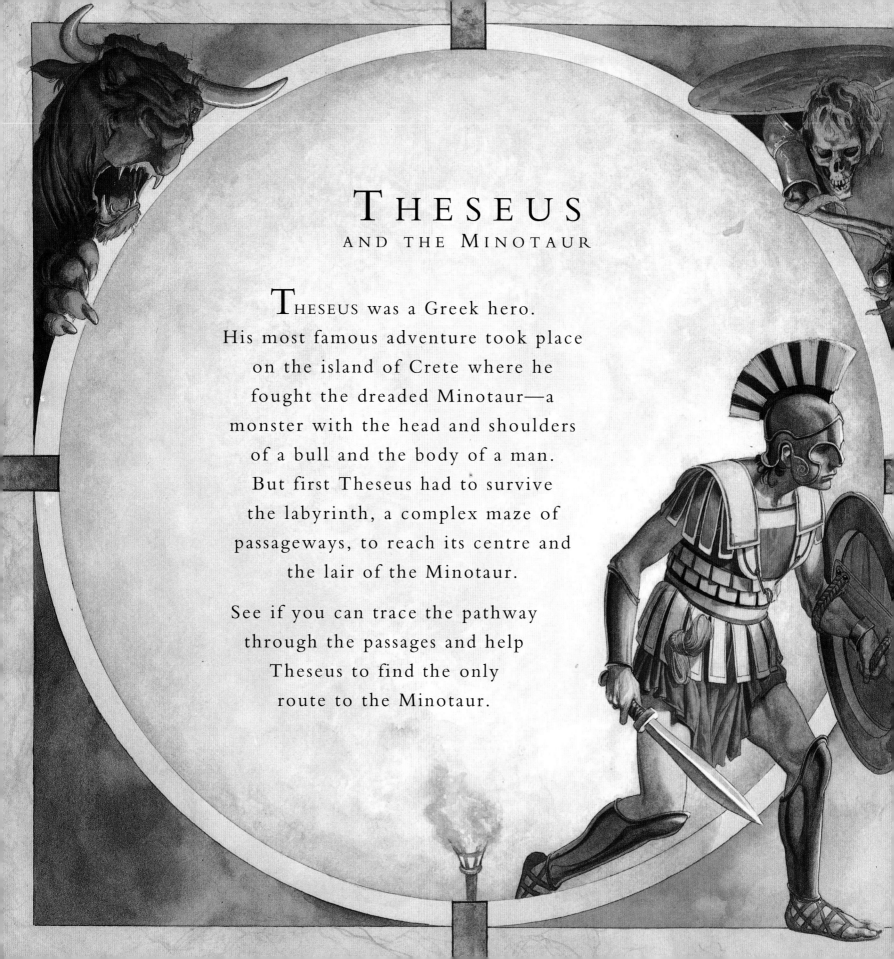

THESEUS
AND THE MINOTAUR

Theseus was a Greek hero.
His most famous adventure took place
on the island of Crete where he
fought the dreaded Minotaur—a
monster with the head and shoulders
of a bull and the body of a man.
But first Theseus had to survive
the labyrinth, a complex maze of
passageways, to reach its centre and
the lair of the Minotaur.

See if you can trace the pathway
through the passages and help
Theseus to find the only
route to the Minotaur.

KING MINOS of Crete demanded that the great inventor Daedalus build him a maze, or labyrinth, that was so clever and complicated that no one could ever find their way out of it. This maze was to be the home of the Minotaur, a terrifying monster, half-bull, half-human, who craved human flesh to eat. The Minotaur's victims were pushed into the labyrinth to wander helplessly in the dark until the Minotaur found them and devoured them.

But King Minos was faced with trying to find enough victims to feed to his monstrous guest. Then, one day, he found a terrible solution. Androgeus, a son of King Minos, was murdered in Athens and, in revenge, King Minos demanded that the Athenians send him seven young men and seven young women every year to cast into the labyrinth.

King Aegeus of Athens was desperate, but there was nothing he could do — there was no one brave enough to try and defeat the Minotaur.

Then, Theseus, who was the son of Aegeus, arrived in Athens. He decided to go to Crete and face the monster. He took the place of one of the youths and set sail with the others in a ship hung with black sails, promising his father that on his return he would change these for white sails so that everyone in Athens would know that his attempt to kill the Minotaur had been successful.

When Theseus arrived in Crete he was brought before King Minos. Beside the King was his lovely daughter Ariadne. She fell in love with Theseus and decided to help the strong Athenian hero. At the door she secretly gave him a sword and a ball of string to carry into the labyrinth.

"The labyrinth is as dangerous as the Minotaur itself," she told him. "Once inside it is impossible to find your way back without help!"

Theseus attached one end of the string to the labyrinth door and then entered the dark corridors. Soon it became darker and darker and he was forced to feel his way along the tunnels. As he went he carefully let out the string behind him. After a long while, Theseus found that the ground was becoming more and more scattered with bones and skulls, the sad relics of the Minotaur's bloody meals. Suddenly he heard a mighty roar behind him. He turned just in time to avoid being gored by one of the beast's huge horns. The monster's sense of smell was so acute that it did not need to see, but without light Theseus was totally blind and had to rely on his sense of hearing alone. He managed to wound the Minotaur and the beast retreated and hid in the darkness. Theseus listened but could hear nothing. Had the Minotaur gone off to die? Suddenly the deafening roar sounded again in his ears. Theseus jumped to one side, knelt down and struck upwards with his short sword, plunging it deep into the monster's heart.

This time he was sure it was dead. Theseus found the end of his string and slowly retraced his steps out of the maze.

When he reached the door, he found Ariadne waiting for him and he secretly took her aboard his ship and sailed back to Greece. He was so happy that he forgot to raise the white sails on his ship. When King Aegeus saw the ship returning all hung with black sails he was so stricken with grief that he threw himself into the sea, where he drowned. That sea has been called the Aegean ever since. And so it was that Theseus finally became King of Athens.

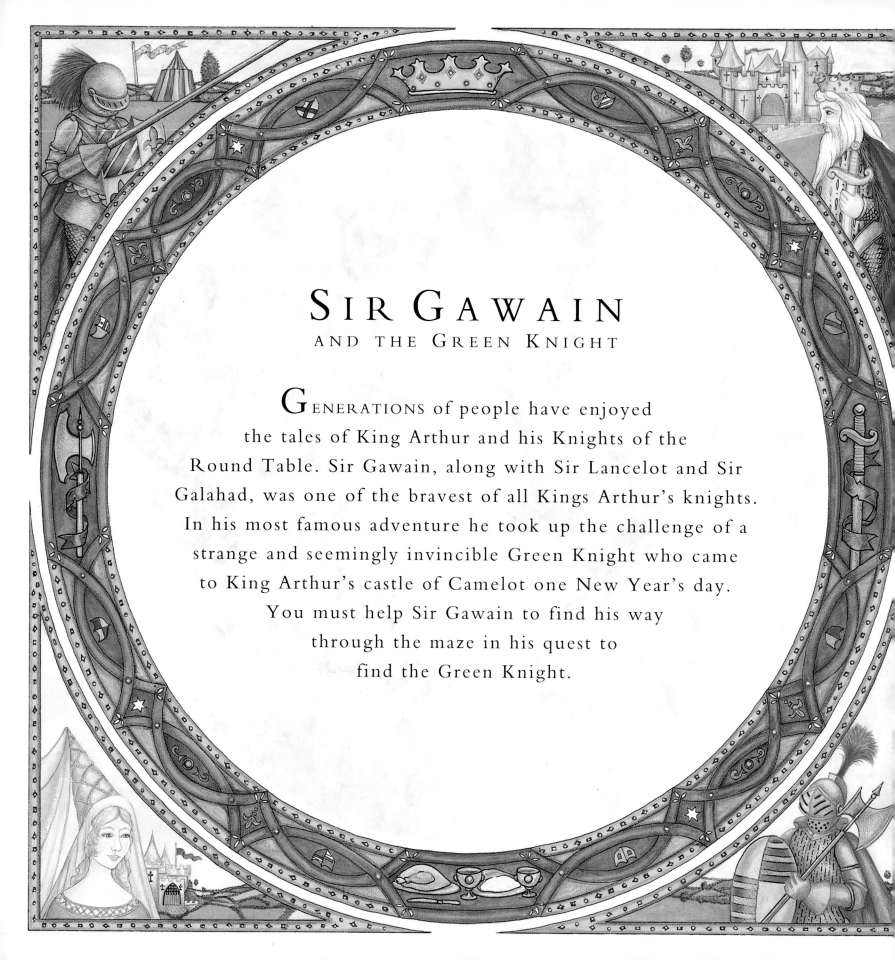

SIR GAWAIN
AND THE GREEN KNIGHT

GENERATIONS of people have enjoyed
the tales of King Arthur and his Knights of the
Round Table. Sir Gawain, along with Sir Lancelot and Sir
Galahad, was one of the bravest of all Kings Arthur's knights.
In his most famous adventure he took up the challenge of a
strange and seemingly invincible Green Knight who came
to King Arthur's castle of Camelot one New Year's day.
You must help Sir Gawain to find his way
through the maze in his quest to
find the Green Knight.

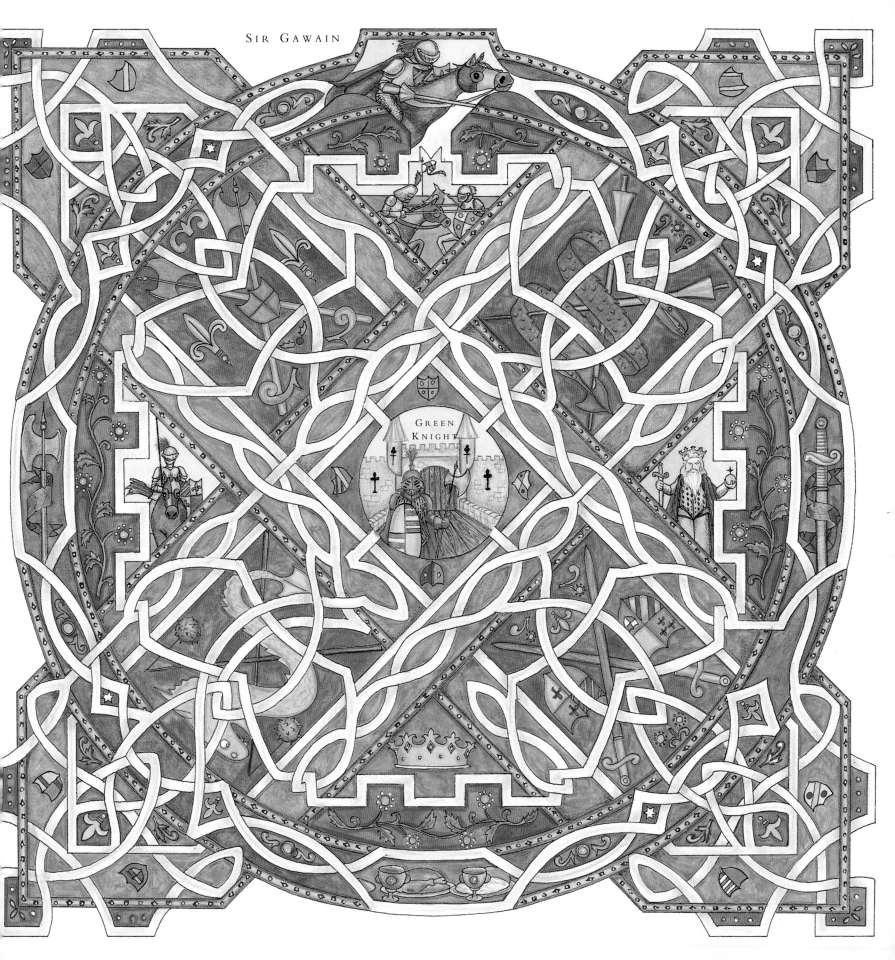

SIR GAWAIN

GREEN
KNIGHT

ONE New Year's Day a strange man rode into Camelot on his horse. He was green from top to toe. His hair, his shaggy beard, and even his face were all bright green. He was the Green Knight.

"Are you the famous knights of King Arthur?" he laughed. "You don't look very brave to me!" This made King Arthur very angry.

"Any of my knights will fight you, if that is your wish," he said.

The Green Knight laughed again.

"Any of your knights who is brave enough may strike me with his sword," he said. "If I am still alive, I will strike him with my axe in one year's time."

Sir Gawain was a brave knight. He took his sword and struck the Green Knight such a fierce blow that his head fell off and rolled on the floor. The Green Knight bent down, picked up his head, and tucked it under his arm.

"In one year, Sir Gawain, you must come to the Green Chapel," he laughed. "Then I shall strike you!"

The year passed. No matter how hard Sir Gawain looked, he could not find the Green Chapel anywhere.

On Christmas Eve he stopped at a castle. The lord of the castle welcomed Sir Gawain warmly.

"You needn't look any further for the Green Chapel," he said. "It is very close. My servant will take you there on

New Year's Day."

Sir Gawain stayed with the lord and his beautiful wife. After several days of festivities, the lord decided to go out to the forest to do some hunting.

"Let us make a bargain, Sir Gawain," he said. "If I catch anything when I am out hunting, I will give it to you. If you receive anything in the castle, you must give it to me!"

The lord rode out, and his wife entertained Sir Gawain. When she left him in the evening, she kissed him goodbye. The lord soon returned and gave Sir Gawain a fine stag. In return, Sir Gawain gave him a kiss. "That is all I have received today!" he laughed merrily.

The next day, the lord's wife was very charming. Sir Gawain thought she was very beautiful, but he did nothing to show it. At the end of the day she gave him two kisses.

That evening the lord gave Sir Gawain a wild boar and Sir Gawain gave him the two kisses in return.

The third day was New Year's Eve. Sir Gawain told the lord's wife that the next day he would have to meet the Green Knight. She looked very worried.

"Take this green girdle, Gawain," she said, giving him three kisses, "It will protect you from harm."

Sir Gawain took the girdle because he was scared of the Green Knight. The lord returned and gave Sir Gawain a fox skin. Sir Gawain gave him the three kisses, but he made no mention of the girdle.

The next day, the servant took him to the Green Chapel. There, the Green Knight was waiting for him.

"Bow your head, Sir Gawain," he said, "I am going to strike you with my axe!"

Sir Gawain bowed his head, but could not help flinching when he heard the axe. Twice the axe came down towards him and twice he flinched away from it. The third time the axe came whizzing down he did not flinch. To Sir Gawain's surprise, it only cut him a little.

"That cut was for not telling me about the girdle!" laughed the Green Knight. Sir Gawain realized that the Green Knight was really the lord. He had asked his wife to tempt Sir Gawain to see if he was a true, brave knight. Sir Gawain had passed the Green Knight's test!